Dolphin Rescue

Written by Roderick Hunt
Illustrated by Nick Schon,
based on the original characters
created by Roderick Hunt and Alex Brychta

OXFORD
UNIVERSITY PRESS

Say the sound and read the words

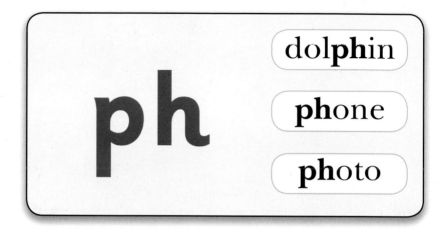

ph

dolphin

phone

photo

ƒ

fin

float

ee

deep

need

keep

ea

beach

team

sea

leave

A grey shape lay on the beach.

"Oh no!" said Gran. "It's a dolphin."
"Why is it lying there?" said Wilf.

"It has lost its way," said Gran.

"It needs to go back into deep water."

Some men got to the dolphin.

"Let's pull it back in the sea," said a man.

Gran ran up to the men.

"No!" she cried. "Leave it alone."

"I will phone the dolphin rescue team," she said. "They will get it back into deep water."

Gran told Wilma to keep all the
children away.

"It is lying on its side," said Gran.
"Get it upright."

Dig holes for its fins.

"Keep it cool," said Gran.
"It needs shade."

"Don't get water in the blow-hole,"
said a man.

A man tried to take a photo of
the dolphin.

Soon the dolphin rescue team came.

The rescue team put the dolphin on a float.

The rescue team took the dolphin
back into the sea.

"I hope the dolphin will be all right," said Biff.

Talk about the story

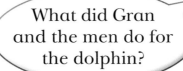
What did Gran and the men do for the dolphin?

What did the dolphin rescue team do?

Have you helped a creature in distress? How?

25

Word jumble

Make the *f* and *ph* words and the *ee* and *ea* words from the story.

ee   s

i   f   n

p   k   ee

m   ea   t

n   d   ee   s

(**ph   i   o   l   d   n**)

(**ea   ch   b**)

(**ee   d   p**)

27

f or ph?

The sound 'f' can be spelled *f* and *ph*. Match the right 'f' spelling to the pictures and complete the word.

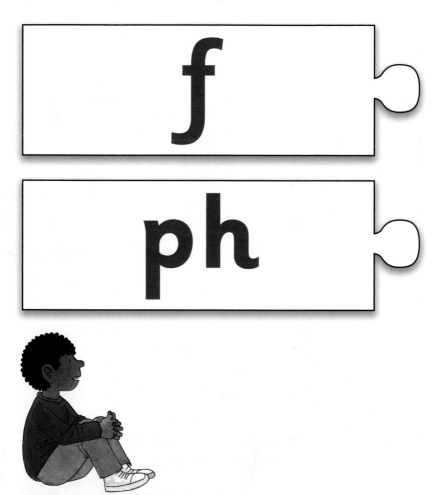

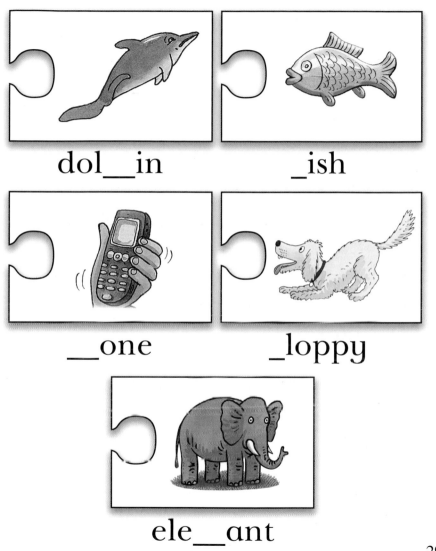

dol__in

_ish

__one

_loppy

ele__ant

A maze

Help the dolphin find its way out to the open sea.

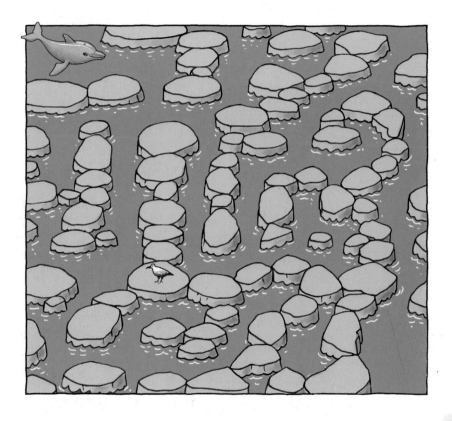